CHARLES WOOD'S

Somerset Quiz Book

HALSGROVE

First published in Great Britain in 2009

Copyright © Charles Wood 2009

British Library Cataloguing-in-Publication Data
A CIP record for this title is available from the British Library

ISBN 978 1 84114 968 4

HALSGROVE
Halsgrove House,
Ryelands Industrial Estate,
Bagley Road, Wellington, Somerset TA21 9PZ
Tel: 01823 653777   Fax: 01823 216796
email: sales@halsgrove.com

Part of the Halsgrove group of companies.
Information on all Halsgrove titles is available at: www.halsgrove.com

Printed and bound by Shortrun Press, Exeter

Contents

Introduction

They called Somerset "the Summer Land". However, my four tender-aged children made many a puddle-splash to disprove it, particularly at weekends or during holidays when school was out. At such times, given half a chance, they chose to sofa-snuggle watching 'the box', endlessly playing fuzzy VHS tapes of 'Wind in the Willows' and 'Rugrats', or getting very cross in games involving a sonic hedgehog.

Change was needed. I felt a compulsive need to slow the process of vegetation for which Somerset was wildly renowned. It came with my undemocratic decision to 'coat-boot-and-bundle' en masse into the rust-bucket car and be off down bumpy tracks on trips of local discovery.

We played 'the map game'. The rules were simple: close one's eyes and finger stab the Ordnance Survey. Where the finger landed we *almost* always went. Everywhere we drove offered something to defy boredom, whether badger cities in the woods or red deer amid Dunkery heather, old ruins on the Black-downs or clamberable bridges over the River Barle.

Slightly further afield, my two sons squabbled to be King Arthur and my daughters did likewise over Guinevere. To tell them that the characters had as much substance as Father Christmas or the Tooth Fairy would have gone down like a lead balloon. But sometimes the truth will out in the county of battles and apples. Quietly and without pressure, snippets of useful knowledge were garnered and became, for me at least, an ongoing habit helpful to documentary filmmaking or radio wittering in defiance of the new age of Blu-ray DVD.

This heady mix, compiled under twelve categories, is intended to entertain – from simples to core understanding, and sporting chance to pure buggerbiddle, a word that's come to mean complete and utter twaddle. Where appropriate, I thought to doodle a few pictures to help the focus.

So, all in all, this quizzical little book delves into a sample of results from narrow lane excursions following my bonnet, snagging goose grass and bracken fern on wing mirrors, rummaging in second-hand bookshops or just chatting to locals in the know. It's my hope that such endeavours enlighten inquisitive grockles and even 'rusty' locals, particularly on days when the rain drips, trickles and soaks.

Wiveliscombe, August 2009.

Simples

1. Somerset is Gwlad yr Haf in Welsh, Gwlas an Hav in Cornish and Bro an Hañv in Breton, which all mean what?
   a)   Place of Apples
   b)   Isle of Blood
   c)   Land of Summer
   d)   Kingdom of Willows

2. What is a 'stoke red'?
   a)   A type of withy
   b)   A cider apple
   c)   A breed of Somerset pig
   d)   The piece of iron used by Exmoor blacksmiths to make a horseshoe

3. What is a hully?
   a)   An eel basket
   b)   A small type of boat used in Bridgwater Bay
   c)   The old name for a sea trout
   d)   A sand martin's burrow

4. In about 500 AD Cadbury Castle was known for being what?
   a)   A royal mint
   b)   King Arthur's 'Camelot'
   c)   A Cistercian monastery
   d)   A Viking fortress

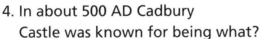

5. What is a 'manchip'?
   - a) The Yeovil word for a limp
   - b) A wedge of holly wood that assists a Quantock forester to fell trees
   - c) The Sedgemoor name for a haw or rose hip
   - d) A jam filled roll local to Bridgwater

6. What words are missing from the following Somerset saying? Any man who stands under an elder tree on Midsummer Eve can see —— and get the wish of his heart. But he will die within the year.

   - a) Dancing hares
   - b) A pot of gold
   - c) The fairies
   - d) A wyvern

7. What word is missing from the following quote from 1797 about Somerset folk by John Billingsley? "The disposition to —- is but too apparent among lower orders."
   - a) Fornication
   - b) Poaching
   - c) Drunkenness
   - d) Celibacy

8. What words are missing from the following rural remedy? "To cure whooping cough, put —— — in a patient's shoes."

    a) A fried mouse
    b) Dried earth worms
    c) Grated red deer antler
    d) Dried stinkhorn fungus

9. What words are missing from the following rustic custom? "If a younger sister happened to marry before the elder one, the latter had to dance in — — if she did not want to die an old maid."

    a) Spring morning dew
    b) A hog's trough
    c) Slippers of rabbit skin
    d) Wookey Hole caves

10. What day of the year in West Somerset is being described? "If your doors are left open, the children with blackened faces will creep in and throw a load of broken crocks all over the floor and try to leave unseen. If the householders chase and catch them they further black their faces with soot, and then give them a cake before letting them go."

    a) All Hallows Eve
    b) Shrove Tuesday
    c) May Day
    d) St Carantoc's Day

11. In her 2007 book *Mendip from the Air* Hannah Firth wrote about 'Priddy Circles'. What are they?

    a) The rural lanes that seem to circumnavigate Priddy village.

    b) Four stone circles contemporary to Stonehenge

    c) Crop circles made by hedgehogs

    d) Circles made up of hurdles, penning sheep at Priddy Fair

12. In 1899 what was towed overland to Porlock from Lynmouth?

    a) Queen Victoria's first motor car

    b) One hundred and ten barrels of shipwrecked vintage cider

    c) A lifeboat

    d) The materials for building St Dubricus's church tower

13. William Prynne, the tireless pamphleteer from Swainswick, was ever the stark disciplinarian. To him men wearing their hair long was "unseemly and unlawful unto Christians," while it was "mannish, unnatural, impudent, and unchristian" for women to cut it short. His writings so enraged the Royal family that they had Prynne's what cut off in 1633?

    a) His allowance

    b) His tongue

    c) His paper and ink supply

    d) His ears

14. By what means did Watchet's St Decuman cross the Bristol Channel from Wales and what did he bring with him?
   a) On a hurdle with a cow
   b) In a coracle with apple pips
   c) In a golden bowl with a mouse
   d) On a dragon with an eel

15. What is the 'Kilve Pill'?
   a) A World War II defence structure
   b) A small stream
   c) An old Somerset aphrodisiac
   d) A large ammonite that can be seen in Taunton Museum

16. In 1968 the travel writer John Hillaby, asked an Exbridge chap what, in his opinion, was the difference between Somerset and Devon. The chap didn't think there was any although on the whole he preferred Somerset. Why?
   a) The cider was better quality
   b) There were larger herds of red deer to be seen
   c) The trout fishing was better
   d) The women were easier

17. Shepton Mallet has Europe's largest what?
   a) Cider plant
   b) Shoe factory
   c) Garden tool manufacturer
   d) Garden gnome manufacturer

18. St Mary's church at Orchardleigh near Frome is unique in England to have what?
    a) Bats in the belfry
    b) A moat around it
    c) A museum of church relics in the crypt
    d) A cock pheasant once appointed vicar

19. In folklore it was officially spring when what happened?
    a) A virgin covered seven daisies with her naked foot
    b) A cuckoo called four times
    c) A stoat caught a hare
    d) A maid spread her legs within a fairy ring of toadstools

20. Whose motto is "Alterum trahe tintinnabula portat"?
    a) Yeovil Town FC
    b) Somerset and Avon Police
    c) Taunton Deane Morris Men
    d) The Luttrell Family of Dunster

21. What is a hunky punk?
    a) A gargoyle
    b) A fat cock pheasant
    c) A bronze age burial mound
    d) A wallflower

22. The roof timbers for the renovation of Stoke Pero church in the late 19th century were brought up the hill from Porlock by what?
   a) Jemima the charabanc
   b) Facawee the traction engine
   c) Apache the carthorse
   d) Zulu the donkey

23. What was bombed by the Luftwaffe on 4 January 1941?
   a) Glastonbury Abbey
   b) A herd of Uphill cows
   c) Butlins in Minehead
   d) SS *Nornen* on Berrow beach

24. What hit the triangular King Alfred's Tower near Bruton in July 1944?
   a) A Canadian aeroplane
   b) A Yeovil helicopter
   c) An American tank
   d) A tornado

25. Which is the highest Somerset town above sea level?
   a) Somerton
   b) Crewkerne
   c) Chard
   d) Dulverton

26. What was Porlock's traditional dish that was potted and commonly sold in Bath during the 18th century?
    a) Shrimps
    b) Hare
    c) Herring
    d) Seaweed mush

27. Who was the pirate, author and scientific observer born in East Coker in 1651 who became the first Englishman to explore or map parts of New Guinea and Australia, called New Holland at the time?
    a) Clinton Rogers
    b) Hallam Moseley
    c) William Dampier
    d) John Pople

28. What did Shepton Mallet estate agent Carole Bohanan become in summer 2009?
    a) Captain of Somerset's Women's cricket team
    b) World mangold hurling champion
    c) Witch of Wookey Hole
    d) World Point-to-Point champion

Core
Education

1. Who was the Georgian dandy with eccentric and scurrilous antics that assumed the self proclaimed title of "King of Bath"?

2. What does Nynehead's 'Cairn of Peace' commemorate?

3. Who faced a battle of character known as 'Rinkagate' begun at Minehead magistrates' court in August 1978?

4. Having habits of frugality, modesty and secrecy the Knights Templar have left little behind. However, what was found hidden in a Templecombe cottage roof in 1950?

5. What thirty-six year old chap was found disguised as a shepherd, shivering in a ditch under a Horton hedge, condemned to death by Act of Attainder, and executed for treason on Tower Hill on 15th July 1685?

6. Chimes play from which church tower at one, five and nine p.m. daily, with a change of tune for every day of the week?

7. What disaster occurred at 9.00 a.m. on the 30th January 1607?

8. George Williams lived in Dulverton and died in 1905. What organisation did he found on 6th June 1844?

9. Which portrait and landscape artist who painted 'The Blue Boy' and 'Lady in Blue', as well as a self-portrait of himself in a tricorn hat, said in Bath in August 1768, "Lord, what can one do such Weather as this, continual rains. My Genius is so dampt by it that I can do nothing to please me"?

10. Which town was known recorded in the *Domesday Book* in 1086 as 'Givele' meaning 'The Noble River'?

11. Which famous philosopher was born in or near Ilchester around 1214?

12. Known as the 'Father' of the modern civil service, Sir Charles Edward Trevelyan, 1st Baronet, KCB published his views of the Irish Potato Famine in the middle of 1840s crisis. He saw the famine as a "mechanism for reducing surplus population", and believed "the judgement of God sent the calamity to teach the Irish a lesson," for being morally evil. Where was the delightful chap born?

13. The first King of Wessex, Cerdic is thought by some scholars to be the basis of the legend of King Arthur and the Knights of the Round Table. Cerdic's original 'headquarters' were in Cerden. What is the town called today?

14. Symbolically named after the first two Greek letters of the word "Christ", a 'Chi-Rho' silver amulet, thought to be from the 5th century, and so held to be among the earliest evidence of Christianity in England, can be seen in Taunton Museum. However, in 2008 analysis at Liverpool University demonstrated that the amulet was a hoax. Where was the amulet 'found' and why was it deemed a hoax?

15. The name 'Frances Countess Waldegrave' was once very familiar in the Radstock area. Who was she?
    a) An owner of race horses
    b) An owner of coalmines
    c) A spiritual healer
    d) A writer of 'racy' romances

16. What have been collected in recent years in buckets in Charlcombe Lane, near Bath?
    a) Walnuts
    b) Horse chestnuts or conkers
    c) Toads
    d) Piles of horse dung

17. Listed in the *Domesday Book* as 'Brunetone', the families Sydenham, Storton and Fane successively owned which manor house near Yeovil, described as the most beautiful house in England and for a few years following World War II was a boys' school?

18. Where will one hear what's agreed to be the finest peal of six bells in England?

19. Which famous cardinal, put in the stocks by Sir Amias Poulett of Hinton St George, held his first cure of souls in the hamlet of Limington in 1500?

20. What industry was founded in Axminster by Thomas Whitty in 1755?
    a) Carpets
    b) Agricultural implements
    c) Military arms
    d) Breakfast cereals

21. What town was called by the Romans, 'Iscalis'?

22. Called the 'English Mozart' and nicknamed the 'Tommasino', who was born at the Abbey Green, Bath on 7th May 1756 and composed no less than twenty concertos for the violin between 1771 and 1776, as well as the 'Shakespeare Ode'?

23. Who was born in Wrington near Yatton in 1632 to Puritan parents of modest means and became one of the greatest philosophers in Europe at the end of the seventeenth century?

24. A famous engineer involved with the Forth Bridge, the Aswan Dam, the Metropolitan underground, a New York subway, and who designed the boat that brought Cleopatra's Needle from Egypt to the Thames Embankment was born in 1840 at Keyford. Who was he?

25. The steep and bumpy Porlock toll road owes its existence to Ada, Countess of Lovelace, the wife of Lord King who had a romantic house and Italianate garden built for her at Ashleigh Combe two hundred years ago. Both house and gardens are now overgrown, hidden in the woods north of the road. Ada was the only legitimate daughter of which poet?

26. What was 'pixy-wording'?

27. What did Herbert Botham, an aeronautical engineer, pass on for his friends to try and swing in the Westland Helicopters wind tunnel at Yeovil in 1981?

28. Looking down from the air with the aid of 6 inches to 1 mile Ordnance Survey maps of the district between Somerton and Glastonbury, according to the 1930s' theories of Katherine Maltwood, Fellow of the Royal Society of Arts, there are prehistoric earthworks and artificial watercourses that delineate numbers of enormous effigies that resemble what arranged in a circle she called 'The Temple of the Stars'?

29. A pair of large ceramic murals by Ned Heywood, depict what on the side of Nailsea's Tesco?

30. Which is England's only residential centre for folk dance and music?
    a) Gauldon Manor
    b) Halsway Manor
    c) Fyne Court
    d) Montacute House

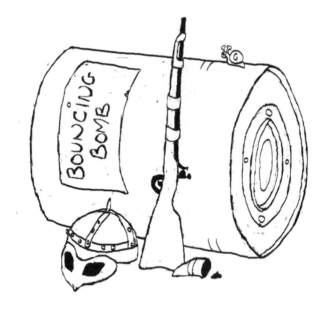

Battling About

1. A battle between Saxons and a thousand Danes took place in 878 near Cynwit that featured in Bernard Cornwell's 2004 novel *The Last Kingdom* and also in *The Marsh King*, a children's historical novel by C. Walter Hodges. What is Cynwit known as today?

2. In the days of Cavaliers and Roundheads, Chewton Mendip, Landsdown, Langort and Marshalls Elm all had English Civil War battles. Place them in their order of occurrence.

3. Who were the Somerset Clubmen?

4. The 'Father' of the RAF was born in Taunton in 1873. Who was he?

5. The army officer credited with organising the Japanese surrender after World War II, Lieutenant Colonel Geoffrey Collingwood Sherman, died in 2009, he was 93. On 12 September, 1945 he had orchestrated the ceremony of Japanese capitulation in Singapore. At the retired officer's memorial service, the same Union Flag used in the Singapore ceremony was flown on the tower of his home village. Name the village.

6. Which plumber was made an Officer of the French Legion of Honour, had a sculpture made of his image by Alan Dun, a poem written in his honour

by the poet laureate, Andrew Motion, and had his portrait painted by Peter Kuhfeld and exhibited at the Royal Society of Portrait Painters Exhibition in London?

7. What was commissioned in 1941 as HMS Birnbeck by the Admiralty as an outpost of the Directorate of Miscellaneous Weapons Development and used for secret weapons testing including the "bouncing bomb"?

8. What was discovered in 2009 by metal detector in a Nether Stowey cottage garden and declared as "treasure" by the Somerset coroner?
    a) Civil War silver in a pot
    b) A Viking hoard of gold
    c) Roman coins in a leather pouch
    d) Coleridge's money box

9. Name the hill topped by an Iron-Age hillfort once known as the Mount of Frogs.

10. Name the 'Highbridge Schindler' who saved the lives of over 10,000 Jews and whose statue can be seen in Highbridge's Market Street.

Local Verbage

1. Where might you find a 'conk' at Somerset cricket's County Ground?

2. What would have been described as 'lippary'?

3. What tree had blossom called 'snag-blowth'?

4. Why might you look upwards to see a 'proud tailor'?

5. What was an 'angle-twitch'?
   a) A carpenter's tool to achieve right-angled joints
   b) A sore knee caused by bursitis
   c) A rabbit warren
   d) A large earthworm

6. Where on a cat would you find a 'vleer'?

7. What would you be doing if you were 'shrigging?'

8. Why might a 'whister-twister' make you feel groggy?

9. In what in the house would you put 'tutties'?

10. What would you feel if you had the 'pew-moanier'?

11. What was a hirdick?
    a) A spade
    b) A robin
    c) An earthenware bottle of cider
    d) A clay pipe

12. What was a pulk?
    a) a small pool of water
    b) A dragonfly nymph
    c) A duck
    d) A bullrush

A Sporting Chance

1. Which ex-Somerset and England player taught Ian Botham how to bowl?
    a) Mervyn Kitchen
    b) Joel 'Big Bird' Garner
    c) Tom Cartwright
    d) Graham 'Budgie' Burgess.

2. Who was born and grew up in Wells, was offered a scholarship to Millfield School at the age of 16 and won the gold medal in the long jump at the 1964 Summer Olympics by breaking the world record, becoming the first-ever British female to win an Olympic gold medal in a track and field event?

3. Name the bowler, his nickname and the match in which 1978 BBC television commentary reported: "Last ball of the match. Three runs required. The last pair together. If (he) bowls another no ball they'll hang him here."?

4. Which Somerset batsmen opened for England in two test matches against the Australians in July 1993?

5. Which rugby club is second only to Bath as the oldest in Somerset?

6. Trained by David Pipe at his stables at Nicholashayne, near Wellington name the horse that won the 2008 Grand National at Aintree.

7. Who of the following former Somerset players did not play International test cricket?
   a) Sir Vivian Richards
   b) Jamie Cox
   c) Vic Marks
   d) Harold Gimblett

8. Name the Frome-born racing driver who in 2003 raced for BAR and whose personal car collection includes a 1956 VW camper van.

Pure
Buggerbiddle

1. What row of stones, each no bigger than large fists and dedicated to a champion jumper from the time of the Monmouth rebellion, can be found in Loxley Woods just off the A39 between Glastonbury and Bridgwater?

2. What were Gog and Magog?

3. A tiny island beside the River Brue, was the site of a chapel of St Mary Magdalene. Someone visited the chapel after the death of his squire and found it guarded by two hands, each holding a sword. Name both the visitor and the island.

4. What place did John Leland, Henry VIII's Antiquary decide was the 'famous toun or castelle' called Camelot?

5. Between Glastonbury and Street is Pomparles Bridge derived from Pons Perilis, the Dangerous Bridge. It replaced a predecessor. What according to Mallory did Sir Bedivere chuck off the original?

6. The Roman general Ostorius was said to have killed hundreds of ancient Britons. Over the centuries a dragon is said to have grown from the corruption of the rotting bodies. The dragon took up residence in an Iron Age hill fort and preyed on the populace until Fulk Fitzwarine, a 13th century knight, slew the creature. Where and on what can the gruesome story be seen depicted?

7. Where has the ghost of a tabby cat been observed padding around and vanishing when it sits down and a white Elizabethan lady been seen sitting in a chair?

8. What Wrington rock is believed to come alive on nights of the full moon?

9. Where did the Devil keep raising gales to blow down an upright cross so that villagers were forced to lay their cross on the ground?

10. What ball was erroneously placed as Lot 67 in the auction of Combe Sydenham furniture and effects in November 1950?

Old Stones

1. What ancient implements made of chert and found in the Blackdown Hills can now be seen in Watchet Market House Museum?

2. Maglemosians, the first immigrants from Denmark, came to Somerset 4,000 years ago. Their 'Burins' were found at Doniford. What were 'burins'?

3. What were the 3,000 year-old weapons found at Battlegore, Williton, and now in the Prehistory Gallery of Taunton Museum, made from?

4. Where are Hautville's Quoit and 'the fiddlers and the maids'?

5. Near Bath is a Neolithic chambered cairn, 98-feet long and 49-feet wide, with multiple burial chambers. It has the curiosity of the left hand door jamb being decorated by an ammonite. What is the cairn called?

6. What and where is the 'Fairy Toot' once known as a place for curing warts?

7. What's the name of the Grade 1 listed narrow stone packhorse bridge over the River Avill in Dunster?

8. Which castle, having a gateway that's still prominent today, was built in the 14th century originally as a manor house for the Montfort family, and fortified between 1370 and 1380 without the appropriate "licence to crenellate" from the king?

9. Cleeve Abbey was founded in the year 1198, by which order of monks?

10. Name the roofless tower that sits on top of Glastonbury Tor.

11. Thirty-four feet by twelve-feet, which medieval chapel was a plague-church and sacred site since Anglo-Saxon and possibly pre-Christian times?

12. Name the 140-foot column finished in 1768 at a cost of £2000 at Curry Rivel from a design by Capability Brown that caused the death of a cow.

13. The chief fisherman of which abbey once lived in the Abbot's Fish House at Meere?

14. During the English Civil war five Somerset castles were returned to their original military purpose. Name them.

15. What is 'Jack the Treacle Eater'?

16. Name the old stone clapper bridge in the Barle River Valley below Hawkridge.

The Literary Landscape

1. Often referred to as the "Last Victorian" and described as "proud, shy, reticent, strong- willed, sweet-tempered, and self-centred," his works included *Poems by Melanter* and *The Bugle of the Black Sea*. Who was he and what was his most famous work that was part written in the bar of the 'Royal Oak' pub in Withypool?

2. Which American poet and playwright, who never lived in Somerset, has a simple plaque commemorating him in St Michael's church, East Coker that reads, "In my beginning is my end. In my end is my beginning"?

3. Name the Exmoor writer and illustrator who for years lived alone in a caravan on Ferny Ball at Landacre and whose book *Living on Exmoor* was described the most significant work to appear about Exmoor since Fortescue's *Story of a Red Deer*?

4. Who in 1797 described his low-ceilinged and dark cottage as "a hovel, a shed, damp and infested with mice"?

5. Which writer living for years in Pilton, and whose works include *Puffball* and *Big Women*, called the area around Glastonbury, "Airhead country"?

6. Who was born at Sharpham Park near Glastonbury in 1707 to a father who was an army officer, drunkard and spendthrift, and a mother who was a judge's daughter; suffered greatly in life from asthma and gout, and apart from innovative literary achievements co-founded London's first police force, the Bow Street Runners?

7. Which prolific novelist, whose work is considered part of the 'Western canon', lived in Bath between 1801 and 1806 and set two novels largely within the city? Also, name those two novels.

8. The film based on the book *Green Dolphin County* won an Oscar for Special Effects in 1948. Which writer, born in Wells in 1900, wrote the book?

9. Which author born in 1903 wrote a diary in Combe Florey in 1956, and who, inspired by John Betjeman's lifetime companion teddy bear named Archibald-Ormsby-Gore, had a book character, Lord Sebastian Flyte, carry a teddy bear named Aloysius?

10. In 1989 the journalist Bel Mooney wrote that she was puzzled by crowds on a late August afternoon and went on to say, "The place could not be *this* popular; everyone on the promenade, sitting in

packed rows, and all staring seaward, as if they had expected some miraculous visitation from the deep." Where was she describing?

11. Which vicar of Combe Florey, and noted as the wittiest man of his time, described his neighbours as looking "very much like other people's neighbors; their remarks are generally of a meteorological nature."? And wrote on 16th August 1842, "There has certainly been some serious mistake about this summer. It was intended for the tropics; and some hot country is cursed with our cold rainy summer, losing all its cloves and nutmegs, scarcely able to ripen a pine-apple out of doors, or to squeeze a hogshead of sugar from the cane."

12. In what decade did the nature writer Roger Deakin write, "Woke to more mist flooding the land, floating the church towers and trees. Then it evaporated into a brilliant, shining blue, and I swam just outside Hambidge in one of the long, straight drains crossing the flat grazing meadows on west Moor like tall mirrors."?

13. Who wrote a sonnet while enjoying a drink in the bar of Porlock's 'Ship Inn' in 1798 that begins, "Porlock, thy verdant vale so fair to sight"?

14. A poem by whom mentioned: "Kilve's delightful shore and Quantoxhead"?
    a) Coleridge
    b) De Quincey
    c) Wordsworth
    d) Byron

15. The 17th-century mystic poetess Elizabeth Rowe, largely unheard of now though she was big in her day, achieved European fame. She retired to Rook Lane House in her beloved home town. Which town was it?

16. Name the retired farmer's wife, born and bred on Exmoor, well-known for her humorous tales about local people in books such as *The Last Word on Exmoor* and *Exmoor Exposed*?

17. Name the author awarded an MBE in 1981 for his services to journalism in West Somerset who wrote books such as *Murder and Mystery on Exmoor* and *Rattle his Bones* (an account of Exmoor workhouses)?

18. The writer of *Teach Yourself Guide to Sex*, *Whale Watcher* and *Youch it Bites* lived in Frome. Who is he?

19. The third and youngest son of a general, who was Joint Secretary of the Society of Authors from 1971 to 1978 and an outstanding champion of authors' rights once living at Langaller, a small run-down farm with no electricity, at Brushford on the edge of Exmoor?

20. The first of a generation to write erotic fiction for the mass market, who was the red-haired beauty nicknamed the 'Montacute tigress' whose 1907 novel *Three Weeks* centred on a younger man and older woman having a passionate affair and making love on a tiger skin?

21. Where was the children's book *The Wild Hunt of Hagworthy*, written by Penelope Lively in 1971, set?
    a) Stogumber
    b) Exford
    c) Winsford
    d) Simonsbath

Truthful Rumours

1. Why was William Edgell of Midsomer Norton so level-headed before he died in 1940?

2. What was discovered in the Brue Valley between Westhay and Shapwick in 1970 by Ray Sweet, a peat digger?
   a) King Arthur's sword Excalibur
   b) King Alfred's brooch
   c) An old trackway
   d) A woolly rhinoceros

3. A skull of what, said to be the finest example of its kind ever found in England, was discovered by William Beard in a cave under Banwell Hill in 1824?

4. What was Thomas Bessie who roamed Wiveliscombe streets in the 1880s?

5. H.J. Prince, a Victorian curate of Spaxton, decided he was the Messiah and in 1846 set up 'Agapemone', or the 'Abode of Love'. Whenever he did his shopping in Bridgwater an acolyte walked ahead intoning "Blessed is he who Cometh in the Name of the Lord." What was Prince's 'Agapemone'?

6. What is the Becket Cup?
   a) A trophy for West Somerset's champion village cricket team
   b) The goblet drunk from at Minehead Harriers Hunt meets
   c) A china teacup for best samphire tart at Halse summer fête
   d) A broken wooden cup of religious nature from Kewstoke

7. Throughout the 1930s and '40s Oliver Messel was a prop designer, the creator of costumes and sets for ballet and stage productions in England's most lavish productions. What were his talents called for in Somerset?

8. Who was the vicar's son whose replica shoes were placed in Odcombe church in 2000?

9. Tatworth's Stowell Mead Court holds an annual candle auction at 'Ye Olde Poppe Inn' for what every April?

10. The reward of the Manor of Mells to a treacherous steward is 'the plum' in which well-known nursery rhyme first published in 1725?

11. A village of two words lies in a narrow valley, near South Cadbury, that belonged to a Norman knight whose name translated as 'Fat-bellied'. Name the village.

12. What is 'Will's Neck'?

13. Which Clevedon-born man established In 1680 that porpoises are mammals and in 1698 dissected a chimpanzee that resulted in the book, 'Orang-Outang' in which he concluded the chimpanzee has more in common with man than with monkeys, particularly with respect to the brain?

14. In 1801 the Quaker and polymath Thomas Young, called the founder of physiological optics and noted for his contributions to the fields of vision and light, was the first to describe astigmatism. Where was he born?

15. What was the purpose of Langport's Annie Tite fund?

16. In August 2009 Jack visited the Magna Housing Association in Williton. Who was Jack?
    a) A hermit who had lived alone in a Dunster beach hut for forty-five years
    b) An African-grey parrot
    c) A pig
    d) A tortoise

Wild Things

1. Montacute Hill was once famous for having Somerset's largest what?
   - a) Rookery
   - b) Oak tree
   - c) Badger sett
   - d) Wood ant colony

2. With a Latin name of Buteo buteo, what makes the sound of a kitten?

3. What is being described at Dunster? "They look as if entangled in an inextricable maze. They go to and fro in regular order, exactly like the fashionable folk in Rotten Row, but the two ranks pass so quickly that looked at both together the vision cannot separate them, they are faster than the impression on the retina."

4. What bird was known as the 'holm-screech' because of its voice and love of holly? It 'plants' mistletoe seeds by cleaning its beak in tree bark crevices after eating the berries that are filled with a sticky substance.

5. What Exmoor creature is a pricket?

6. What animal makes a wontwiggle?

7. What would someone be after, if they went glatt hunting?

8. A Titty-todger was what in old Somerset verbage?
   a) A new born piglet
   b) A calf
   c) A wren
   d) A buxom lass

9. What is the native fish of Exmoor rivers?
   a) Rainbow trout
   b) Brown trout
   c) Two spot goby
   d) Rock salmon

10. Which falcon, after a 2,500 mile journey from south of the Sahara, catch hatching dragonfly nymphs on Shapwick Heath between April and May each year?

11. What was Molly who turned up exhausted on Burnham Beach in June 2007?

12. Somerset County Council gives instructions for scrub in Old Cleeve not to be cut back because of what creature locally known as the 'seven-sleeper' having a penchant for the hazel trees?

13. In the verge of Withybed Lane, Cucklington near Wincanton, what small creatures once known as 'stare-basins' are protected by conservationists?

14. What is the name given to the courting and mating season of Exmoor's wild red deer?

15. Becoming extinct in the UK in 1979, what now thrives particularly at Green Down, the Somerset Wildlife Trust's nature reserve in the Poldens, one of the best sites in the world to see it?

16. Ham Wall near Glastonbury has become a notable site for large flocks of what to congregate at dusk on autumn evenings?
    a) Jacob Sheep
    b) Avocets
    c) Starlings
    d) Flamingos

17. What was shot at Watchet in 1897?
    a) A puma
    b) A crane
    c) A white stag
    d) A porcupine

18. Between 1836 and 1906, 4320 what were shot on Exmoor's Holnicote and Winsford estates?

19. What bird was called a 'Skir-devil'?

20. What are said to be rarer than the Giant Panda and were "discovered" by James Cossar Ewart, a Scottish zoologist?

21. 10 million what descended on a Coombe St Nicholas farm in summer 2009?

Face the Music

1. Which pop group formed in 1976 by singer Phil Fursdon and Clive Wilson and formerly known as Alive n' Kickin came from Weston-super-Mare?

2. Who in 1999 wrote the song 'NFB' an abbreviation for 'Normal For Bridgwater'?

3. Which singer/songwriter, raised by her quarryman father and her artist mother, grew up on a sheep farm in Yeovil and released her debut album 'Dry' in 1992?

4. With tickets costing £1, Sam Apple Pie and Marsupilami amongst the entertainment, and advertising "all food at fair prices, ox roast and all farm's milk free," what kicked off with Stackridge on 19th September 1970?

5. Who met while working at Butlins in Minehead within the first three years of it opening, became friends and formed the group The Spectres?

6. Name the football song sung by Gary Johnson and others that shifted 3,500 copies in three days and was based on the American Civil War song 'Two Little Boys' made famous by Rolf Harris.

7. Which of the following was a Wurzels single?:
   a) Chirpy Chirpy Sheep Sheep
   b) Cider White Swan
   c) Drink Up Thy Zider
   d) All Together, Plough

8. Consisting of Geoff Barrow, Beth Gibbons and
   Adrian Utley, which band released the album
   'Dummy' in 1994 that was ranked number 419 on
   Rolling Stone magazine's list of the 500 greatest
   albums of all time?

Gurt Screen and Corner Box

1. Which TV sitcom featuring the character of Margo Leadbetter first aired in 1979 was filmed at Cricket St Thomas?

2. Which film starring Johnny Depp was filmed in Wells and partly at Montacute House?

3. The Oscar-winning film adaptation, starring Emma Thompson and Hugh Grant, of which Jane Austen novel was partly filmed at Montacute House and in Montacute village?

4. Which 2008 TV mini-series starring Gemma Arterton was filmed in Frome and Bath?

5. Which railway station was renamed Fal Vale in the 1931 film 'The Ghost Train' that starred Jack Hulbert and Dame Cicely Courtneidge from a play written by Arnold Ridley, better known as Private Godfrey in Dad's Army?

6. Which Sherlock Holmes adventure, filmed by Canadians, was shot in 2000 at Montacute House?

7. The 1986 TV series 'The Monocled Mutineer' starring Paul McGann was filmed in the town called in Old English "the sea-lake enclosure." What is the town called today?

8. *Cider With Rosie*, the memoirs of Laurie Lee and 'Eastenders: Perfectly Frank' were both partly filmed for TV on which Somerset construction?

9. 'Berkeley Square', a costume drama series about three nannies in Edwardian England was filmed in 1997 in which Mendip village?

10. England's smallest city, Wells, was featured in what 2007 film starring Simon Pegg?

11. Which Bryan Adams record, number one for 16 weeks in the UK singles charts in 1991 and the soundtrack for 'Robin Hood Prince of Thieves' had its music video filmed at Kilve Beach and Holford Glen?

12. Name the Monty Python sketch featuring John Cleese as Hitler set in West Somerset.

13. Freshford, Monkton Combe, Limpley Stoke and Combe Hay where all locations for which 1953 film starring Stanley Holloway and an old engine?

14. What steamy thing links the TV adaptions of The 'Lion, the Witch and the Wardrobe' (1988), Poirot: 'The Cornish Mystery' (1989), and Miss Marple: 'The Mirror Cracked' (1992)?

15. A location for the Oscar-nominated 'Elizabeth': The Golden Age starring Cate Blanchett, the former Axbridge Rural District Council gave what to the National Trust to celebrate the Festival of Britain in 1952?

16. Which children's TV comedy starring Tony Robinson was filmed at Cleeve Abbey and on Exmoor?

17. A 1964 mock documentary written by Alun Owen featuring Crowcombe Heathfield station starred which famous four, and what was the film's title?

18. A series of novels by Stephen Potter set in The School of Lifemanship were adapted for the 1960 film 'School for Scoundrels', starring Alastair Sim, Terry-Thomas, and Ian Carmichael. Where were the books set and the opening sequence of the film shot?

19. Name the 2000 film, shot on the Quantock Hills and at Nettlecombe Court, about the Romantic Poets directed by Julian Temple and starring John Hannah as William Wordsworth.

20. The 1998 BBC TV documentary series 'Doctor's Orders' was an insight into the life of Dr Paul Slade, a Somerset GP and his surgery. In which town was the series set?

Answers

Simples Answers

1. c) Land of Summer.

2. b) A cider apple. One of the best for the job.

3. a) An eel basket. It's a peculiarly shaped long wicker trap.

4. a) A royal mint. Not for sucking, but for making money.

5. d) A jam filed roll local to Bridgwater. Not now as popular as a cream cake.

6. c) The fairies.

7. d) Celibacy.

8. a) A fried mouse.

9. b) A hog's trough.

10. b) Shrove Tuesday or Pancake Day on which children would sing: "Tippety, tippety tin, Give me a pancake and I will come in. Tippety, tippety toe, Give me a pancake and I will go."

11. b) Four stone circles contemporary to Stonehenge.

12. c) A lifeboat. In January 1899 *Forest Hall*, a three-masted ship floundered in the Bristol Channel in the worst storms of a lifetime. Unable to put to sea at Lynmouth the only chance the crew had of saving the *Forest Hall* was to tow the lifeboat *Louisa* with horses and muscle power thirteen miles to Porlock. The rescue mission was successful and all lives were saved.

13. d) His ears.

14. a) On a hurdle with a cow. The cow is said to have always followed the saint about supplying him with milk.

15. b) A small stream.

16. d) The women were easier.

17. a) Cider plant. Owned by Constellation Brands, the Shepton Mallet plant produces Blackthorn and Gaymer's Olde English cider, and Babycham.

18. b) A moat around it. St Mary's is often referred to as 'the church on the island'. Its remoteness means there is no electricity supply, so services are candlelit and the organ has to be pumped by hand.

19. a) A virgin covered seven daisies with her naked foot.

20. c) Taunton Deane Morris Men. The motto means "pull the other leg, it's got bells on."

21. a) A gargoyle.

22. d) Zulu the donkey. He plodded twice a day for many months during 1897/8 bringing the timber from Porlock and his portrait hangs on the church wall.

23. b) A herd of Uphill cows. Uphill was made a decoy town laid out by Shepperton Film Studios to protect Weston-super-Mare airfield.

24. a) A Canadian aeroplane. It was a Noorduyn C-64A Norseman. Five US airmen died.

25. c) Chard. The town sits at an altitude of 397 ft (121 m).

26. d) Seaweed mush or laver. Once collected, edible seaweed is repeatedly washed to remove sand then boiled for hours until it becomes a stiff green mush that can be preserved for about a week. It was the mush that was packed into a crock and sold as "potted laver". Apparently it was a favourite dish of Samuel Coleridge.

27. William Dampier. He was also the first person to circumnavigate the world three times and was described as "Australia's first natural historian".

28. The Witch of Wookey. She was given the name 'Carla Calamity' after beating 300 rivals for the £50,000 a year job.

Core Education Answers

1. Richard Beau Nash who died in 1761 aged 87. He dressed with an exaggerated elegance, dared to be different and had a huge impact on Bath society by advocating greater social integration. He established a new code of conduct for more respectability in public places by banning swearing and relaxing the unwritten rules of integration. 'Beau' created a platform for social change.

2. The World Ploughing Championships held in a Nynehead field in 1971. Locals call the monument 'The Can of Peas'.

3. Jeremy Thorpe, the former leader of the Liberal Party. A former male model Norman Scott claimed that he had a gay relationship with Thorpe between 1961 and 1963, at a time when homosexual acts were still illegal in Britain. Scott alleged that Thorpe had threatened to murder him if he spoke about their affair. In October 1975, while walking a friend's Great Dane, "Rinka", on Exmoor, Scott was confronted by Andrew "Gino" Newton, a former airline pilot, who was armed with a gun. Newton shot and killed the dog, which had been lent to Scott for protection, then pointed the gun at Scott, but it apparently failed to go off. The subsequent scandal embroiled Thorpe and became known as "Rinkagate". The case brought Thorpe's career to a sudden and messy end.

4. A painting of Christ's head, though some think it's John the Baptist, probably dating from around 1280. Now it can be seen in the nave of St Mary's church in Templecombe.

5. James Scott, Duke of Monmouth, the son of Lucy Walter, Charles II's lover. His army of rebels had been defeated at the Battle of Sedgemoor in the first week of July 1685 by the forces of King James II, led by Louis Duras, Earl of Feversham. Executioner, Jack Ketch, took several blows of the axe, and before a dismayed and murmuring crowd, Monmouth's head left his body with the assistance of a knife.

6. The church of St George in Dunster.

7. A Tsunami that came up the Bristol Channel causing seawater to lap Glastonbury Tor 21 miles inland. Accounts from eye witnesses described "huge and mighty hilles of water, tumbling one ouer another," and "many howses overthrownw, sundry Chrystyans drowned, hundreds of rudder cattell and horse pertshed, and thowsands of sheep and lambs lost."

8. The Young Men's Christian Association, the YMCA.

9. Thomas Gainsborough.

10. Yeovil.

11. Roger Bacon.

12. Taunton in 1807. Trevelyan became Governor of Madras in 1859.

13. Chard.

14. Shepton Mallett. The silver dated to the 19th century.

15. b) An owner of coalmines. Rail travellers often remarked on her name being on coal trucks in the 1870s. Frances set the fashion for the peerage being connected to 'trade' without shame.

16. c) Toads. The problem for the migrating toads, as well as frog and newts, making the journey downhill towards the breeding ground is that they become trapped by the high garden walls of Charlcombe Lane. The walls funnel the toads down the lane where they are often killed or injured by the traffic. Volunteers put the amphibians into buckets and walk across the lane.

17. Brympton d'Evercy.

18. Queen Camel.

19. Cardinal Wolsey. Few men born without noble blood had as much power as Wolsey during the time of Henry VIII.

20. a) Carpets.

21. Ilchester.

22. Thomas Linley the younger. On 21st April 1770 Mozart's father, Leopold, writing to his wife Anna Maria said, "In Florence we found a young Englishman who is a pupil of the famous violinist Nardini. The little Englishman, a most charming boy, brought his violin to where we stayed and played all afternoon with Wolfgang accompanying him on the piano." In 1784 Mozart said, "Linley was a true genius." Linley drowned in a boating accident aged 22.

23. John Locke 1632-1704.

24. Sir Benjamin Baker.

25. Lord Byron. The remains of walls and follies of the garden can be seen on the walk from Porlock Weir to Culbone.

26. 'Pixy-wording' was gleaning for the apples that remained after the cider apple-harvest was done. Villagers used to say the fairies held the sprinkling

of stray apples on the trees to make a hoard. Although the apples were sparse, when put together the stragglers made 'a tidy vew'.

27. The cricket ball that swung prodigiously allowing his son Ian Botham to take five wickets against the Australians at Lords. Despite doing rigorous tests at Westland's, no reason could be found why the ball had swung so much.

28. Zodiacal creatures. They differ very little from the constellation figures, and the corresponding stars fall within their boundaries. Some believe it's around these archaic 'Nature Giants' that the Arthurian romance snowballed. Take for example Leo. Made up of 'Sedgemoor Forest', the 'lion's' ear is Muncombe Hill, its lower jaw is Worley Hill, the head is Caple Wood and the neck is Hurcot.

29. The history of the Nailsea glass industry.

30. b) Halsway Manor.

Battling About Answers

1. Cannington. The battle took place on Bleadon Hill. Legend has it that the Danes landed at Uphill, and left their fleet to pursue the locals, who with the exception of one infirm lady, fled. The woman starving hungry had sought food on board the Danish ships. Finding the ships deserted, she cut their moorings. The Danes returned from the chase to discover their vessels adrift and borne to sea by the tide. As a result the locals took courage, and defeated the Danes on Bleadon Hill.

2. Marshall's Elm, August 1642, Chewton Mendip, June 1643, Lansdown, July 1643, Langport, July 1645. Marshall's Elm, near Street, was the first skirmish of the war in Somerset. A small Royalist force of about 80 horse moving from Wells towards Burrow Bridge to bar the crossing of the Parrett, met and defeated a body of Parliamentary recruits of more than 600 men. Seven Parliamentarians were killed on the spot, and eighteen died later from wounds. The Parliamentarians were routed at Chewton Mendip. Landsdown was the most sweeping victory the Royalists ever won. At Langport the Parliamentarian forces under Fairfax routed Goring's Royalists.

3. The Somerset Clubmen were local farmers and yeomen, who were sickened with the plundering and the 'pressing' of men into either the

Parliamentarian or Royalist Civil War army, and wanted peace above all else. However they were vital to the Parliamentarian war effort. Fairfax could spare little time for them but meeting them at Middlezoy in July 1645 he promised that, if they agreed not to help the Royalists, he would pay for all the supplies he needed and ensure that his troops committed no offences against the locals.

4. Lord Hugh Montague Trenchard. He was born at Windsor Lodge on Haines Hill in Taunton, on 3 February 1873. He died in 1956.

5. Long Sutton.

6. Harry Patch, the last survivor of the WWI trenches. He grew up in Coombe Down, near Bath, and fought in the Battle of Passchendaele, in Ypres. He never spoke in public about the Western Front until he turned 100. One of his favourite awards was that of the Freedom of the City of Wells, where he had lived for many years. He died in July 2009 aged 111.

7. Birnbeck Pier in Weston-super–Mare.

8. a) Civil War silver in a pot. An earthenware pot containing silver items buried for safekeeping during the Civil War was discovered 18 inches below the surface. The items bore the letters

CGA, the initials of Angel Grey, the then owner of Stowey Court, and his wife, Catherine. The 17th century collection included a goblet, four spoons and salt and pepper holder.

9. Brent Knoll.

10. Major Frank Foley. He was born in Highbridge and MI6 recognise him as one of its greatest officers. This quiet and modest man was Britain's top spy in Berlin and in his 'cover' job as Passport Control Officer in Berlin, according to one Jewish aid worker, saved "tens of thousands" of people from the Holocaust. Jewish families with documents and visas faked by Frank escaped from Nazi Germany after Kristallnacht, the Night of Broken Glass, the anti-Jewish pogrom on 9th and 10th November 1938, and before the outbreak of the Second World War.

Local Verbage Answers

1. In the stands. A conk means a crowd of people.

2. The weather. It meant wet and rainy.

3. The blackthorn, today we know the tree's blossom as 'may'.

4. It's a bird, the goldfinch.

5. d) A large earthworm.

6. In its fur. Vleer means flea.

7. Trimming a tree.

8. Whister-twister means a blow to the side of the head.

9. A vase. Tutties was a general name for flowers.

10. Ill. Pew-moanier was pneumonia.

11. A robin.

12. A small pool of water.

A Sporting Chance Answers

1. c) Tom Cartwright MBE. He played for Somerset 1970 - 1976 and won five England caps 1964 - 1965.

2. Mary Rand.

3. Colin Dredge, 'The Demon of Frome'. The match was the Gillette Cup semi-final Somerset v Essex on 16th August 1978. With the scores level at the end Somerset won by losing fewer wickets.

4. Mark Lathwell.

5. Wiveliscombe. The club was founded in August 1872. Out of interest Philip Froude Hancock was born in Wiveliscombe and is still on record as being the heaviest man ever to play for England. He was also a founder member of the Barbarians.

6. Comply Or Die.

7. b) Jamie Cox. A former Somerset captain and an Australian who played for the Tasmanian Tigers. He was expected to play for Australia as an opening batsman in 2001, however, the position was given to Justin Langer.

8. Jenson Button.

Pure Buggerbiddle Answers

1. Swayne's Leaps.

2. Gog and Magog were Ancient oak trees also known as 'The Oaks of Avalon'. They once grew in a grove with other oaks from which an avenue ran up towards Glastonbury Tor. According to a book dating from 1829 'Glastan-byrie' means the 'Hill of Oaks'. Both trees were cut down in 1906. Magog was 11-feet in diameter and had more than 2000 season rings which it made older than Christianity.

3. King Arthur. Beckery.

4. South Cadbury.

5. Excalibur.

6. Norton Fitzwarren. A sixteenth-century rood screen stands in All Saints' church that depicts the tale.

7. King John's Hunting Lodge, Axbridge.

8. The Waterstone.

9. Banwell Hill, where there is a clearly defined cross of earth and stone about 120 feet by 129 feet across the arms.

10. Sir Francis Drake's cannonball. It was apparently fired from Plymouth to Monksilver as a warning to Elizabeth Sydenham not to marry another suitor.

Old Stones Answers

1. 200,000 year-old Palaeoliths, better known as hand-axes.

2. Burins were flint tools used for cutting antler or bone.

3. Bronze. The weapons included axes, dagger, spear-heads, arrow-heads and knives.

4. They are Megalithic standing stones at Stanton Drew, part of the second largest stone circle complex in Britain, that got their names from legend. According to Wade and Wade in their 1929 book *Somerset*, the quoit was formed when "a large stone was hurled by Sir J. Hautville, whose effigy is in Chew Magna Church, from the top of Maes Knoll." 'The fiddlers and maids' were a wedding party turned to stone by the Devil. The stone circles are the dancers, the avenues are the fiddlers and the Cove is the bride and the groom with the priest at their feet.

5. Stoney Littleton Long Barrow or Wellow Tumulus.

6. An extensive oval barrow these days covered with ash trees and shrubs in the village of Nempnett Thrubwell. In 1929 it was described as "a remarkably fine tumulus of masonry, said to have

been one of the finest in Britain, in the chambers of which skeletons have been discovered. A few vestiges of it now only remain, the rest has been used as a lime-kiln."

7. The Gallox Bridge. It used to be called the Gallows Bridge.

8. Farleigh Hungerford Castle.

9. Cistercians, also called 'The White Monks'. Cleeve Abbey was founded by William de Romare, with emphasis on a life of manual labour and self-sufficiency.

10. St Michael's Tower. Built in the 1360s it replaced an earlier one destroyed by an earthquake on 11 September 1275, which was felt in London, Canterbury and Wales.

11. Culbone. The smallest complete church in regular use in England.

12. The Burton Pynsent Monument. Dedicated to the memory of Sir William Pynsent a highly successful businessman in the thriving Somerset cider trade. When the government of the day was considering taxing cider more heavily, William Pitt the Elder opposed the proposals. Sir William was so grateful for the politician's support that he changed his will and

left the Burton Pynsent estate to Pitt. The viewing platform at the top is no longer accessible. The stairs were closed after a cow somehow managed to climb the stairs and fall to its death.

13. It was once the abode of the chief fisherman of Glastonbury Abbey. Now the only surviving monastic fishery building in England, the Abbot's Fish House was used for salting and preparing fish that were caught in Meare Pool.

14. Bath, Bridgwater, Dunster, Nunney, and Taunton. Nunney fell in 1645 when a few cannon balls demolished a wall. Built in 1373, Nunney was said to have been based on the Bastille in Paris. John Leland described it as a "praty" building. In 1646 the works around Bath and Bridgwater were slighted. Taunton was the only one garrisoned by Parliament who lost it and then regained it under Robert Blake. Dunster was the last to fall in 1651.

15. Jack the Treacle Eater is the name given to a stone arch, topped by a round tower with a human figure standing on one leg on the very top. The most easterly of the four Barwick Follies near Yeovil and built in the mid 1700s, the tower was probably a dovecote. Somerset County Council purchased all four Barwick follies for £5.00 in the 1990s.

16. Tarr Steps.

The Literary Landscape Answers

1. Richard Doddridge Blackmore, 7 June 1825 – 20 January 1900, commonly referred to as R. D. Blackmore. *Lorna Doone* published in 1869.

2. Thomas Stearns Eliot, better known simply as T.S. Eliot. The poet was buried in East Coker after his death in 1965. He chose to have his ashes taken to St Michael's church as this was the village his ancestors emigrated from. The quoted lines come from his poem 'East Coker':

3. Hope L. Bourne.

4. Samuel Taylor Coleridge, and was said about his cottage in Nether Stowey where he lived for a couple of years. He moved into it with his wife, Sara, and baby son, Hartley, to be close to his patron Tom Poole and to concentrate on writing.

5. Fay Weldon CBE.

6. Henry Fielding. His most famous novels were *Joseph Andrews* in 1742, and *Tom Jones* in 1749.

7. Jane Austen. The two novels set in Bath were *Northanger Abbey* and *Persuasion*.

8. Elizabeth Goudge.

9. Evelyn Waugh. Lord Sebastian Flyte and Aloysius appeared in *Brideshead Revisited*.

10. Minehead.

11. Sidney Smith (1771-1845) who became rector of Combe Florey in 1729. He described country life as "a kind of healthy grave".

12. 1990s. Roger Deakin wrote the piece in October 1997.

13. Robert Southey. He later became poet laureate.

14. c) Wordsworth.

15. Frome.

16. Norma Huxtable.

17. Jack Hurley. Born in Williton in 1913, he retired in 1980 as Editor of the *West Somerset Free Press* after having spent fifty years with the paper. He died in 1983.

18. Trevor Day.

19. Victor Bonham-Carter. He died in 2007. Writing in *The Independent* obituaries Mark Le Fanu opined that Victor's "two-volume *Authors by Profession*

(1978-84) is the most comprehensive history ever written of the evolution of authorship as a business. In elegant prose, laced with anecdotes, it traces the fragile economics of surviving as a writer, the development of copyright and the perennially tricky - and therefore fascinating - nature of relations between authors and publishers."

He was part of the 28-year campaign to secure Public Lending Right, under which authors receive a small payment each time one of their books is borrowed from a public library. His years of speaking engagements and tireless lobbying culminated in legislation in 1979 and the annual payments made to authors since 1984. One of his last books, *The Essence of Exmoor* (1991), is an analysis of Exmoor since the formation of the National Park in 1954. In 1996 he published his autobiography, *What Countryman, Sir?*

20. Elinor Glyn. A former inhabitant of Montacute House, she also travelled extensively and had success in Hollywood. An affair with Lord Curzon of Kedleston, the tenant of Montacute House, began with a tiger skin. After hearing of *Three Weeks* and its subsequent performance on stage, Lord Curzon, as a mark of his appreciation, sent her a tiger skin from a beast he had shot and killed

himself during his time in India. The gift appears sufficient to have wooed her. Elinor Glyn died in 1943.

21. a) Stogumber.

Truthful Rumours Answers

1. William Edgell was a flat-earther. He wasted his life honouring a promise to prove his dad's pet theory that the earth is flat and astronomers wrong. Spending night after night watching the sky through a steel tube in his garden that pointed at the Pole Star, he calculated the star was five thousand miles away and the sun only ten miles across.

2. c) An old trackway. Now called 'The Sweet Track' after its discoverer, and dating from the 39th century BC the track has been claimed to be the oldest road in the world. It mainly consisted of oak planks laid end-to-end for nearly one-and-a-quarter miles.

3. The skull of a great cave bear.

4. A 'winged' cat. As a kitten Thomas Bessie appeared normal but then went on to develop fur-covered pigeon-sized wings. In 1899 a photograph of the tom cat appeared in the *Strand Magazine* and it became a star. Thirty years later correspondence still appeared in the national press about the Darwin-inspired theory of the evolution of a new cat species.

5. 'Agapemone' was a love nest for Prince, his chums, and a whole harem of ladies who brought substantial endowments with them. To the horror of prudish society, Prince deflowered a 16-year old called Zoe on the chapel altar in front of his devoted congregation of acolytes, who called the event the "Great Manifestation." Although Prince died before Queen Victoria, his last follower survived until 1950.

6. d) A broken wooden cup of religious nature from Kewstoke. Found hidden in Kewstoke church and now in Taunton Museum, the cup is rumoured to have been sold to Woodspring Priory by the monks of Canterbury, claiming that it had caught the blood of Thomas à Becket at the time of his murder in 1170. Two of the murderers, Reginald Fitzurse and Richard Brito, came from Williton. Legend has it that both are buried facing north in unhallowed ground on Brean Down.

7. Oliver Messel was called upon to ingeniously disguise WWII pillboxes, just in case the Germans invaded. Some posed as railway signal boxes, others as water-towers, haystacks and newsagents. A pillbox near Cad Green was even made to look like a bus shelter complete with fake timetables.

8. Tom Coryate (1579–1617), who called himself both "The Legge Stretcher" and "The Peregrine of Odcombe." Born at Crewkerne, he set out from Odcombe in 1608 and walked to Venice and back. He is considered by many to have been the first Briton to do a Grand Tour of Europe, a practice which became a mainstay of the education of British upper class men in the 18th century. In five months he covered 1,975 miles in one pair of shoes and is often credited with introducing the table fork, as well as the word 'umbrella' into England. Tom was described as a strange looking, freakish, dwarf-like man, with a heart large enough to take on the world. "The shape of his head was like a sugar loaf inverted."

He wrote his memoirs in a book with the extraordinary title, *Coryates Crudities, Hastilie gobled up in five moneths travels in France, Savoy, Italy, Rhetia, commonly called the Grisons country, Helvetia alias Switzerland, some parts of high Germany and the Netherlands; newly digested in the hungrie aire of Odcombe in the County of Somerset, 1611.* Apparently it proved very popular.

9. Tenant rights to watercress beds. The Stowell Mead Court is an ancient custom and a private affair. Only people who own or tenant certain properties have a right to bid or be present. A lit inch-long tallow candle is burnt. The last bidder before the

candle gutters and dies is the tenant for the ensuing year.

10. Little Jack Horner. Horner was a steward on the jury that convicted Richard Whiting, the last abbot of Glastonbury, on a trumped-up charge of embezzlement and treason. The unfortunate abbot had refused to surrender his abbey to Henry VIII. On 15th November 1579, Whiting was tied to a hurdle, dragged up Glastonbury Tor and hanged, drawn and quartered.

11. Compton Pauncefoot. Compton meant narrow valley and the Norman was called 'Pauncefote'.

12. The highest point of the Quantocks (1261 ft).

13. Edward Tyson (1650 -1708) commonly regarded as the founder of comparative anatomy.

14. Milverton.

15. A Victorian charitable trust established by local worthy Annie Tite to promote chastity. Langport had scores of young women becoming pregnant from lustful sailors coming ashore. Any girl who presented herself to the town doctor on her wedding day and was proved to be a virgin could claim a sum of money. No Langport girl ever made a claim. The fund is now used for education grants.

16. A pig. Jack was an Oxford Sandy and Black. A second prize rosette winner at the Royal Show, he had escaped from a local farm. "All I saw when he came in was this huge beast," said the housing association receptionist. "I thought he was someone coming in to use the computer or to pick up some information on swine flu."

Wild Things Answers

1. a) Rookery. It was not just the largest in Somerset, but also in the West of England. The writer Llewelyn Powys wrote in 1941 his childhood memory of what he called "the King-rookery'" and "at the hour the lamps were being lit, it was scarcely possible to hear oneself speak in the Montacute streets so great would be the clamour set up by the hosts of birds that were passing across the sky."

2. Buzzard. The bird "mews" as it effortlessly sails over Somerset's countryside scanning the ground below for prey.

3. Clouds of midges on the River Avill. The words are those of Richard Jeffries.

4. Missel or Mistle thrush. The name refers to the bird eating mistletoe.

5. A two-year old male deer or buck before the antlers branch. Pricket means spike.

6. A mole. A wontwiggle is the Somerset word for a mole tunnel.

7. Conger eel. Glatt hunting in the abundance of rock pools went on along the coast from Watchet to the

Parrett. In 1947 Maxwell Fraser wrote: "The great attraction of Kilve for 'those in the know' is the glatting-hunting for conger eels with 'fish-dogs,' and very exciting sport it is, too. It's very rare these days."

7. c) A wren.

8. b) Brown trout. Rainbow trout were introduced from North America and occasionally escape from fish farms and reservoir stock. Rock salmon, alternatively known as dogfish, and goby live in the sea.

10. Hobbies. The hobby is the best flier of all falcons and one of Britain's rarer birds. They can be recognised by their slate-coloured back, dark crown, black 'moustache' and red-brown thighs.

11. A sub-adult Atlantic yellow-nosed albatross from the Tristan da Cunha Islands. There had only been two other reported sightings of the species within an area covering Europe and North Africa, and both were well out to sea at the time. Molly was released back into the wild from the top of Brean Down. Video footage of her can be found on YouTube.

12. Common dormouse.

13. Glow-worms. They are now rare in Somerset due to use of pesticides.

14. The rut. Beginning in September, the rut last for about three weeks, and the countryside echoes to the stags' bellowing roars and the clashing of antlers.

15. The large blue butterfly. Ecologists discovered the butterfly was dependent on red ants. The female butterfly lays eggs on wild thyme plants and the larva falls to the ground, where it is found by the ants. The larva attracts red ants by secreting a sweet 'milk' from its honey gland. The ants take the larva back to their nest where it both feeds and feeds on the abductors. After hibernating through winter and spring the larva turns into a pupa then a large blue butterfly.

16. c) Starlings. Ham Wall is a newly created RSPB wetland, which provides a safe home for many rare species, including water voles and otters.

17. b) A crane, the feathered sort not the mechanical. The crane was seen as a bird of omen. Cranes have not bred in Somerset for over 400 years. Happily, under the Great Crane Project run by the The Wildfowl and Wetlands Trust and the RSPB young cranes are to be released onto the Somerset Levels in autumn 2010.

18. d) Black grouse.

19. Swift.

20. Exmoor ponies, also known as Celtic ponies. They are now believed to be the oldest and most primitive of the British native ponies, as well as the purest, and are directly descended from the ponies that migrated from North America across the prehistoric land bridge.

21. Ladybirds. They arrived to feed off aphids on sedum plants grown for eco-roofing.

Face the Music Answers

1. Racey.

2. Peter Bruntnell, a New Zealander. During an interview at the time he recalled: "A couple, who are friends of mine, ran a particularly rough pub in Bridgwater, and the landlady was telling me one day that the doctors in Bridgwater use the abbreviation NFB when describing their test results for slightly disturbed local patients."

3. Polly Jean Harvey, professionally known as P.J. Harvey.

4. The first Glastonbury Festival at Worthy Farm, Pilton. Also on the bill were Marc Bolan, Ian Anderson, Quintessence and Al Stewart. The festival was sparsely attended due to being badly advertised and poorly organised, but the site was said to be "nice". The decision to change the festival date to around summer solstice proved to be a good one.

5. Francis Rossi and Rick Parfitt. After several changes to the band name they became Status Quo in late 1967.

6. 'Yeovil True' by Yeovil F.C. Released as a single in May 2007 it went straight in at number 36 – two places above Pink and three higher than The

Strokes. Gary Johnson, who managed the Third Division club at the time, told BBC Sport: "We were very pleased with the song and the fans have taken it to their hearts. It was only meant to be a bit of fun, but we played it at a couple of home games and our supporters seemed to like it, so we decided to record it."

7. c) Drink Up Thy Zider. Written by Adge Cutler and released in 1966 the single led to national fame and number 45 in the UK charts.

8. Portishead.

Gurt Screen and Corner Box Answers

1. 'To the Manor Born'.

2. 'The Libertine' (1996), the story of John Wilmot (Depp), a.k.a. the Earl of Rochester, a 17th century poet who famously drank and debauched his way to an early grave, only to earn posthumous critical acclaim for his life's work.

3. *Sense and Sensibility.*

4. *Tess of the D'Urbervilles.*

5. Camerton.

6. *The Hound of the Baskervilles.*

7. Somerton.

8. Clevedon Pier.

9. Priddy.

10. Hot Fuzz.

11. Everything I Do I Do it For You.

12. The North Minehead By-Election.

13. 'The Titfield Thunderbolt'.

14. All had scenes filmed on the West Somerset Railway.

15. Brean Down.

16. 'Maid Marion and Her Merry Men'.

17. The Beatles - John Lennon, Paul McCartney, George Harrison and Ringo Starr. 'A Hard Day's Night'.

18. Yeovil. The opening sequence of the film was shot at the now demolished Yeovil Town Station.

19. 'Pandæmonium'.

20. Minehead. The surgery was Irnham Lodge.